The Snow Queen

A play

Ron Nicol

based on the story by Hans Christian Andersen

Samuel
New York ·

ISBN 0 573 16503 3

Please see page vi for further copyright information

CHARACTERS
(in order of speaking)

First Troll
Second Troll
Third Troll
Fourth Troll
Fifth Troll
Sixth Troll
Old Troll
Gerda
Kai (pronounced Kay)
Grandmother
Snow Queen
First Child
Second Child
Third Child
Fourth Child
Enchantress
Wild Crow
First Soldier
Second Soldier
Sergeant
Tame Crow
Princess
Prince
Twin Ladies-in-Waiting
First Robber
Second Robber
Third Robber
Old Hag
Robber Girl
Reindeer
Lapp Woman
Finn Woman

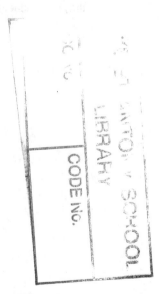

CHARACTERS
(non-speaking)

Lords, Ladies, Gentlemen, Courtiers, Ladies-in-Waiting, Gentlemen-in-Waiting, Ladies' Maids, Handmaids, Housemaids, Parlour-maids, Chamber-maids, Scullery-maids, Lackeys, Flunkeys, Footmen, Servingmen, Servants, Servants' Servants, Servants' Servants' Boy, i.e. as many people as possible; **Robber Band, Snow Queen's Ice Attendants, Ice Creatures, Guardian Angels**.

The **Penguin** has no real part in the story, and penguins belong in the Southern Hemisphere anyway. However, it provides a very small part for the tiniest/youngest member of the group, although it can be omitted.

PRODUCTION NOTES

The Snow Queen has been written with amateur drama groups and youth organisations in mind. Companies vary in what they have available, and many have limited resources. The play can be staged as simply or as elaborately as you wish, but should be as imaginative as possible.

Size of company is not too important because there are opportunities for doubling or even trebling several roles, and there can be any number of Trolls, Courtiers, Robbers, Attendants, Ice Creatures and Guardian Angels.

The action takes place on an empty stage, or in almost any space. Furniture and properties have been suggested, but certain items can be dispensed with if not considered essential. Furniture should be set and struck as part of the action to help each scene flow into the next, and lengthy scene changes must be avoided.

Lighting can be basic or elaborate depending on resources. Fades to black-out for a few seconds are sufficient for scene drops, and together with the scene changes help to keep the performance moving. A snow projector is very effective for adding that touch of magic, and can be used in several scenes. Music could be added for scene links and for background atmosphere in some scenes.

The story takes place in Denmark, Lapland, and Finland but costumes can be authentic or as simple as necessary—lots of furs and blankets. The Reindeer (one person or two) and the Crows provide a challenge for costume makers.

The final battle between the Ice Creatures and the Guardian Angels could be seen as representing the struggle between Good and Evil and should be imaginatively staged or perhaps choreographed for dancers. The Troll and Robber dances may be omitted if preferred.

COPYRIGHT INFORMATION

(See also page ii)

ACT I

The Lights go up on an empty stage

Several Little Trolls enter. They are strange childlike creatures with long fingers and pointed ears, dressed in outlandish ragged clothes. They dance wildly, eventually collapsing in exhaustion

First Troll That were great! I 'joyed that.
Second Troll Yeah—good, wannit?
Third Troll There's better fings to do 'n that.
Fourth Troll Yeah—wot mischief c'n we do?
Fifth Troll Find some yoomins and tease 'em.
Sixth Troll Better'n that—find yoomin *chilluns*!
Second Troll Chilluns—that's better!
Third Troll Much better!
Fourth Troll (*rising*) Where'll we find chilluns round 'ere?
Fifth Troll (*rising and sniffing the air*) I wonder…
Sixth Troll (*rising and sniffing, turning towards the audience*) Hey, look!
Fifth Troll Where?
Sixth Troll There! (*He points at the audience*) Out there! Lots of 'em!
Fifth Troll Yeah! (*He calls to other Little Trolls*) Hey, you lot! C'mere!

The Little Trolls advance and peer out at the audience

Sixth Troll Yoomins!
All Yeah!
Second Troll N' chilluns!
All Yeah!
Third Troll Yoomin chilluns!
All Yeahh!
Fourth Troll Lots of 'em.
All Yeahhh!
Fifth Troll Undrids of 'em!
All Yeahhhh!
Sixth Troll Wot'll we do to 'em?
Second Troll Pinch 'em…
All Yeahhhhh!

Third Troll Poke 'em…
All Yeahhhhhh!
Fourth Troll Punch 'em…
All Yeahhhhhhhh!
Fifth Troll Pull their hair.
All Yeahhhhhhhhh!
Fifth Troll (*pointing*) There's one wiv pigtails—let's pull 'em. Make 'er
    squeal!
Fourth Troll Heh heh! I loves pullin' pigtails—let me do 'em! (*He pushes
    Fifth Troll*)
Fifth Troll (*pushing Fourth Troll*) I seen 'er first!
Fourth Troll Do it togevver—one pigtail each!
Fifth Troll Yeah!

The Fourth and Fifth Trolls are about to climb into the audience

First Troll (*anxiously*) You can't. It's time for school.
Second Troll Spoilsport!
Third Troll Goody goody!
Second Troll Teacher's pet!
Third Troll Get 'im!
First Troll No! No! Noooooo!

*The Little Trolls turn on the First Troll. They fight, yelling, "Pull his ears
off!", "Poke his eye out!", and similar troll-like expressions. The Sixth Troll
keeps a lookout. The First Troll is on the ground*

Sixth Troll Look out! Here's the Headie!

The fight goes on—the First Troll is underneath the other trolls

    (*Panicking*) Stop it, you lot!

    *The Old Troll, an ancient creature with a long white beard, and carrying
    a huge book, enters* UC

The Sixth Troll stands aside and pretends nothing is happening

Old Troll What's going on here?
Sixth Troll Nuffink.

*The Little Trolls get up and try to look innocent, except the First Troll who
is still writhing on the ground. The Little Trolls stand in front of the First Troll
to hide him from the Old Troll*

Old Troll I said—"what's going on?"
All Trolls Nuffink!

As the Old Troll stares them out, they all slowly move aside

Old Troll (*seeing the First Troll*) What are you doing down there?
Second Troll Gettin' up!

The Little Trolls snigger

Old Troll What happened?
First Troll (*getting up and trying to speak*) Them—they wuz…
All Trolls (*drowning out First Troll*) We wizzn't doin' nuffink!
Old Troll (*to First Troll*) I'll speak to you later. (*He turns away*)

The First Troll makes a face at the others. Angry muttering from the other Little Trolls. The Old Troll turns

I'll speak to you *all* later!

The Little Trolls mumble rebelliously

In fact, I think I'll speak to your mothers!

This quietens the Little Trolls

Get to your places!

Grumbling, they sit in a semi-circle round the Old Troll C, facing upstage

Now. Are you all sitting comfortably?
Trolls Yes, Teacher.
Old Troll (*to the Little Trolls and the audience*) Then I'll begin. Now listen! All of you! Listen! It's time to begin our story—and when we come to the end, you'll know more than you do now. (*He opens the book*) Once upon a time…

The Little Trolls groan

Listen! Once upon a time there was a troll—a very old troll—even older than me. Listen! He was an evil troll—the most evil of them all. Now, he invented a mirror. A magic mirror! It had the power to make everything good and beautiful that was reflected in it look small and ridiculous.

Everything bad and ugly was made bigger and much more horrible. But one day, little trolls—naughty little trolls just like you—took that mirror and broke it! Broke it into hundreds and thousands and millions and billions and trillions of pieces. The pieces were smaller than the smallest grain of sand, and the wind scattered them all over the world. Now, any teeniest weeniest tiniest littlest piece that got in someone's eye made that someone see only the bad things in other people and none of the nice things at all. Now, listen—most terrible of all—if a splinter pierced someone's heart—that heart would turn into a lump of ice!

As it begins to snow, the Little Trolls scatter. They re-enter and set up a door frame L of C, a rocking chair and a small table to make a basic room setting R, as the Old Troll continues the story

Now, in that long ago time, in a big city, there lived two children. Their names were Gerda and Kai, and they lived with Gerda's Grandmother in this little house...

The Old Troll and the Little Trolls fade into the shadows as Grandmother enters R, sits in the chair, and starts to knit

Gerda enters the room excitedly R and runs "outside" through the door to L

Gerda Kai! Kai! Come and see!

Kai enters R

Kai What is it, Gerda?
Gerda It's snowing! Look—it's snowing! (*She calls through the door to Grandmother*) Grandma, come and see!

Grandmother rises and goes outside

Kai It's snowing, Grandma! It's snowing! Look!
Grandmother Yes, the white bees are swarming.
Gerda What do you mean?
Kai The snowflakes, silly—they look like white bees.
Gerda So they do. Big fat bees!
Kai Do snowflakes have a queen bee—like real bees, Granny?
Grandmother Yes—she's called the Snow Queen. She flies high up in the clouds where no-one can see her. And no-one *wants* to see her because people say she's all made of ice—dazzling, gleaming ice.

The Light dims as the Snow Queen enters UL *unseen, and stands in the shadows*

(*Shivering*) Ooooh! It's suddenly got colder! Come on—it's too cold to play outside. You can come out again when the snow stops.

They go through the door. Grandmother sits in the rocking chair. Gerda and Kai sit on the floor at her feet

Gerda Tell us about the Snow Queen, Grandma. Please!
Grandmother Well now, let's see. Ah yes—sometimes on a cold winter night she flies through the city streets. She peers in at the windows and breathes on them with her frosty breath—then the glass freezes over, as if it's covered with icy flowers.
Kai Yes—I've seen that!
Grandmother It's so cold she'll probably be looking in the windows tonight.
Gerda (*looking round nervously*) She can't come in here, can she?
Grandmother Oh Gerda, of course she can't!
Kai (*bravely*) Just let her try! I'll put her on the stove and melt her!

The Snow Queen laughs quietly in the shadows L, *and moves downstage*

Gerda What was that?
Kai What?
Gerda I thought I heard someone laugh.
Grandmother (*reassuringly*) There's no-one there, child.

Kai goes to the door and looks out

Kai It's still snowing.

The Snow Queen looks sharply at Kai and away again. Kai clutches his chest

   Ouch!
Gerda What's wrong?
Kai Something hit me in the chest!

The Snow Queen looks sharply at Kai and away. Kai puts his hand to his eye

   Ow!
Grandmother What is it?
Gerda What's happened?

Kai I've got something sharp in my eye now.

Grandmother Let me see. (*She brings Kai back into the room, and looks in his eye*) Look up. Look down. No, I can't see anything.

Kai It's gone. I can't feel anything now.

Gerda Let *me* look!

Kai (*turning away*) There's nothing to see.

Gerda It must hurt. Are you sure you're all right?

Kai (*irritated*) Oh, don't fuss! It's gone now.

Gerda I was only trying to help...

Kai (*pushing her away*) I don't *need* any help!

Grandmother Kai! Don't be so nasty!

Kai (*angrily, imitating her*) "Kai, don't be so nasty!" There's nothing wrong with me! Leave me alone!

Grandmother Goodness me! Sometimes I don't understand you at all!

Grandmother exits UR, *annoyed*

Gerda takes a picture book from the table and approaches Kai as he stands with his back to her

Gerda (*trying to make friends*) Kai. Look at this picture book—it's full of flowers...

Kai Picture books are for babies!

Gerda I'm *not* a baby!

Kai I'll show you something *much* better! (*He goes through the door, reaches out, and catches a snowflake in his cupped hands. He brings it back inside*) Look at this snowflake. It's marvellous—like a star. It's perfect. Much nicer than stupid old flowers...

Gerda (*triumphantly*) Until it melts!

Kai looks at his now empty palm, and turns away. Gerda pulls him round and thrusts the book at him

These flowers are lovely too, and *they* don't melt. Look at these roses...

Kai grabs the book roughly and points at the pictures

Kai (*nastily*) That one's being eaten by a worm, and this one's got a nasty insect on it, and that one's dying! They're really *ugly*!

Gerda They're not! They're not! (*Plaintively*) You like roses...

Kai I don't now. Flowers're stupid! (*He throws the book away*)

Gerda starts to cry

What're you crying for? It makes *you* look ugly! Get away from me!

Kai pushes Gerda away and rushes off UR

Gerda Kai! Where are you going? Kai! Wait for me…

Gerda follows Kai out

The Snow Queen laughs and steps out of the shadows to DL

Snow Queen (*to the audience*) You know what's happened, don't you? You remember the pieces of glass from the mirror—the troll mirror that makes everything look ugly. Poor Kai! He's got a little piece of that glass in his eye, and another in his heart. It doesn't hurt now, but they're there. Soon his heart will be a lump of ice! Put me on the stove and melt me, would he? Ha! He'll learn, he'll soon learn.

The Snow Queen exits L

The Little Trolls remove the furniture and exit

Kai enters R *with a sledge, followed by Gerda*

Gerda Kai! Wait for me!
Kai Why should I?
Gerda Where are you going?
Kai None of your business!
Gerda I want to come with you.
Kai Why?
Gerda I *always* play with you. I love you, Kai!
Kai So what! You're just a baby…
Gerda Kai—please—where are you going?
Kai I'm going sledging in the big square…
Gerda Can *I* come?

The Snow Queen enters UL. *She watches, unseen by the children*

Kai No! Go home. Go on! I don't want you! (*He pushes Gerda away*)

Gerda exits R, *crying*

The Snow Queen approaches Kai, who shivers as she nears him

Snow Queen Ah! Here you are…

Kai (*turning, a bit frightened*) Do I know you?
Snow Queen No, but I know you. (*Softly*) Better than you think.

Kai shivers and wraps his arms round himself

What's wrong?
Kai I'm cold. Right to my bones.
Snow Queen Yes, you must be freezing. (*She takes his face between her hands, looks deeply into his eyes, and kisses him gently on the forehead*)
Kai Ow! You're like ice...
Snow Queen But are you still freezing?
Kai (*surprised*) No—no—I don't feel cold now.

The Snow Queen looks hypnotically into Kai's eyes for a long time, then drops her hands, turns, and moves away L

Please...

The Snow Queen stops, without turning round, a smile on her lips

Where are you going?
Snow Queen Why should I tell you, little one?
Kai I—I'd like to come with you.
Snow Queen (*turning and smiling*) Why should I let you?
Kai (*eagerly*) I know the multiplication tables, and I can do mental arithmetic, and fractions, and I know the dates of kings and queens, and the capital cities of lots of countries, and how many in—inhab—inhabitants there are in different towns...
Snow Queen That's clever—but it isn't enough, you know.
Kai (*pausing, then in a rush*) You're perfect—like a snowflake. You're beautiful...
Snow Queen (*smiling, slowly*) You really *do* want to come with me, don't you?
Kai Yes!
Snow Queen Why?
Kai (*hesitantly*) I don't know. (*He touches his heart and shivers*) I *have* to— something's making me...
Snow Queen Ah! You sense it—the power!
Kai (*eagerly*) If you let me come, I'll do anything you want!
Snow Queen I've a long way to go...
Kai That doesn't matter—I want to see the world! I want to see all the snow...
Snow Queen There's snow here.
Kai I mean the kind at the North Pole—miles and miles of it!

Snow Queen You'd come all the way to the North Pole?
Kai Oh, yes! Do you know how to get there?
Snow Queen We could travel in my sleigh—would you like that?
Kai Yes! Oh, yes! You mean—I can come with you?
Snow Queen Yes. (*She blows a kiss towards him*)
Kai (*clutching his chest*) Ouch! It's like an icicle in my chest! My heart's
    frozen! I'm dying!
Snow Queen No, you're not—but that went straight to your heart. Now, no
    more kisses, or I might kiss you to death. Here, let me wrap my cloak round
    you. (*She wraps her fur cloak round Kai*) How do you feel now?
Kai (*drowsily*) It's like sinking in a snow drift...
Snow Queen Aren't you afraid to come away with me?
Kai No. I *want* to.
Snow Queen What would your Grandmother say? And your little Gerda?
Kai (*drowsily*) Gerda? I don't know any Gerda...
Snow Queen Ah! You've forgotten them already. Good! Now—come!
    Quickly!

The Snow Queen exits L *with Kai*

Gerda and Grandmother enter R

Gerda Kai! Kai!
Grandmother Kai! Where are you?
Gerda He was here—that's his sledge. Kai!
Grandmother He said he was going sledging, but he can't...

Children with Children sledges enter

Gerda Where's Kai!
First Child He isn't with us...
Second Child He was going to come and play...
Third Child But he didn't turn up...
Fourth Child We *saw* him though...
First Child In a beautiful big white sleigh...
Second Child With someone all dressed in white fur...
Third Child With a white fur hat...
Fourth Child It looked like everything was made of ice...
First Child They went down the street...
Second Child And out the city gate...
Third Child And up and up...
Fourth Child Into the sky...
First Child Into the snow clouds...

All Children And then they just disappeared!

They look up into the sky and then exit, followed by Grandmother

Gerda, crying, sits on the edge of the stage DC *as if on a river bank*

The Old Troll and Little Trolls enter upstage, unseen by Gerda

Old Troll No-one knew what had really happened—they thought the children were just telling tales. All winter many tears flowed. Gerda cried hard and long because people said Kai was dead. They said he'd fallen in the river and drowned. Oh yes, those winter days were long and dark, but the spring came at last, and warmer sunshine...

Gerda (*looking up, softly*) Dear sun—you're shining as brightly as you can, but you can't warm my heart! Kai's dead!

Trolls (*whispering from the shadows*) We don't think so.

Gerda Dear swallows—you fly way up high, but I have to stay down here. Kai's dead and gone!

Trolls (*whispering from the shadows*) We don't think so.

Gerda River—did you take my friend? Is he dead?

Trolls (*whispering from the shadows*) We don't think so.

Gerda Look, I'm wearing my red shoes. Remember, I gave them to you as a present so you'd give him back—but when I threw them in, you just washed them back to me. Don't you want them?

Trolls (*whispering from the shadows*) We don't think so.

Gerda They say he fell in and drowned, but if you won't take my red shoes I don't think I believe them. I think he's alive. (*She pauses*) I'm *sure* he's alive. (*She rises*) I *know* he's alive! (*She thinks*) I'm going to follow you, river—maybe you'll lead me to Kai.

Gerda exits L

The Enchantress enters UC. *She is wearing a large sun-hat decorated with flowers, and carrying a bowl of cherries. She supervises the Little Trolls as they cover the stage with a carpet of grass and flowers, and set up a little gate*

When ready, the Little Trolls fade into the shadows. The Enchantress examines one or two of the flowers and then becomes aware of the audience

Enchantress (*sweetly*) Good evening, dear children. My, my, how lovely you look—just like my garden of beautiful flowers. Mind you, I can see one or two weeds, but never mind. We haven't met before, so I'd better make a small confession. I'm an enchantress, but you mustn't be fright-

ened. I don't make spells—I only do a little magic just to pass the time. I'm
not wicked—not a witch! I'm quite nice, really. I live here all by myself,
all alone. Nobody ever visits me. I wish I had a little child of my own.
Perhaps one of you would like to live with me? No? You're sure I couldn't
persuade you...

Gerda enters R *through the gate*

The Enchantress turns

Oh my, oh my! A little girl! (*She smiles and beckons to Gerda*)

Gerda crosses to her

However did you wander so far into the wide world, my dear?

Gerda (*weeping*) I've been following the river—but I can't find him!

Enchantress You poor little child! (*She puts her arm round Gerda and
draws her downstage*) Come now, tell me who you are and how you got
here.

Gerda I'm Gerda. I'm looking for my friend Kai. He's only a little boy and
he's disappeared.

Enchantress (*soothingly*) Hm! Hm!

Gerda We've known each other since we were babies, and we play together
all the time—well, we used to. He's never gone away on his own before.
Have you seen him?

Enchantress No, my dear. He hasn't come by, but I'm sure he'll be along
soon.

Gerda I *must* find him!

The Enchantress wipes Gerda's tears with a flowery handkerchief

Enchantress Now, now, you shouldn't be sad, my dear. Listen, you'll be
hungry. I've some lovely cherries here—you must try them...

*Gerda sinks down, takes off her shoes and rubs her feet. The Enchantress sits
beside her*

My my, you're tired out, you poor child. That's right—make yourself
comfortable. Now, taste these, my dear.

As Gerda eats, the Enchantress combs Gerda's hair with a golden comb

Well now, I've been longing to meet such a sweet little girl! We're going
to get along so well. We'll live very happily together, you'll see.

Gerda sleeps, leaning against the Enchantress

   The Old Troll enters

Old Troll Ssssh! Listen! The Enchantress wants to keep Gerda for her own. That comb's a magic one, you see—it makes Gerda forget little Kai. The old woman doesn't mean any harm, but she's afraid Gerda will remember, and run away. So Gerda stayed all summer long in the old woman's garden, never thinking of Kai or her Grandmother. But then the autumn came…

   The Old Troll helps the Enchantress to rise, and they exit upstage, leaving Gerda sleeping

   Cawing off R, and the Wild Crow enters noisily, flapping his wings

Wild Crow Caw! Caw! Caw! (*He sees Gerda*) Caaaww!!

Gerda wakes

   Good day!
Gerda Hallo.
Wild Crow Tell me, little girl, why are you out here all alone in the wide wintry world?
Gerda Winter! Is it really winter?
Wild Crow Nearly. Very nearly.
Gerda (*confused*) You said I was alone. I *am* alone. But I *shouldn't* be. I should be—I should be—I—it's no use, I can't remember *what* I should be doing.
Wild Crow You can't remember. That's sad. I often have that problem.
Gerda I'm supposed to be looking for something—or someone…
Wild Crow Caw! I'm only a poor crow, but I've got an idea. Why don't you ask these children who you're looking for?
Gerda Why didn't I think of that? (*To the audience*) Children! Please! Tell me where I'm going. Who am I looking for?
Wild Crow (*reacting to the audience*) Caw! Caw? Kaw? Kai? Kai!
Gerda Kai! That's it! I'm looking for Kai! He's disappeared, you see, and I must find him! I must get away from here!
Wild Crow If you'll excuse my saying so—there's a slight problem. This garden belongs to an Enchantress—and she won't let you go.
Gerda Can't you help me?
Wild Crow Me? Caw! I'm only a poor crow—what can *I* do?
Gerda Please, Crow, please!
Wild Crow Don't upset yourself. I'll see what I can do. Caw! Well, anyway, I'll do my best—which is more than most people do.

Gerda We'll just have to think…

Wild Crow I'm not much good at thinking…

Gerda Of course you are—you thought of asking the children who I was looking for, didn't you?

Wild Crow So I did! Caw! Perhaps I'm not so stupid after all!

Gerda Course you aren't! So—think of something.

Wild Crow (*after a pause*) Well, I can think of lots of things…

Gerda What? What?

Wild Crow But I can't think of anything to help!

Gerda We could ask the children to help us fool the Enchantress…

Wild Crow (*looking off*) I'm afraid there isn't time for that!

Gerda Why not?

Wild Crow Because she's just coming down the path. Caw! Get behind me! Quick! (*He stands in front of Gerda and spreads his wings to hide her*)

The Enchantress enters upstage

Enchantress What are you doing? Get away from here! Get out of my garden! Nasty nasty horrid crow!

Wild Crow Nasty horrid crow! Well I never! Caw! (*He controls himself and gives a little bow*) I do beg your pardon, madam. I didn't mean to trespass… (*He starts to edge away, keeping Gerda shielded behind him*)

The Enchantress moves downstage, trying to see behind the Wild Crow

Enchantress Wait! Wait! Have you seen a little girl? She was here!

Wild Crow A little girl? Now, let me think. Have I seen a little girl? Caw! (*He moves downstage, still shielding Gerda and making sure the Enchantress can't see her. He winks at the audience, and encourages their participation, ad libbing if necessary*) 'Scuse me, children, I need a bit of help! Now, if there was a little girl standing in front of me I could see her, couldn't I? But if she wasn't standing right in front of me, I couldn't see her, could I? Well—she isn't, so I can't, can I? Caw! I can't see a little girl, can I? (*He winks at the audience and shakes his head*)

Gerda peers from behind the Wild Crow, shaking her head

(*Turning to the Enchantress*) I'm sorry, madam, I *can't* see a little girl.

Enchantress (*to the audience*) Can *you* see a little girl?

The Wild Crow shakes his head. Gerda stays out of sight

Wild Crow See! They can't see her either.

Enchantress (*advancing on the Wild Crow*) But you *have* seen her, haven't you? Come on, you can't lie to me.

The Wild Crow edges round the Enchantress, keeping his wings spread with Gerda hiding behind him

Wild Crow Well—er—caw! I'd tell you if I would—I mean, I could if I would—er—would if I could. Caw—I'm all confused!
Enchantress (*suspiciously*) What are you hiding behind your back?
Wild Crow Caw?
Enchantress Step aside, Crow.

The Wild Crow steps to one side. Gerda moves with him

No! The other way!

The Wild Crow steps to the other side. Gerda moves with him

(*Ominously*) Crow! You're hiding something! What is it?
Wild Crow Caw! Run! Run!

Gerda dodges as the Wild Crow flaps about and obstructs the Enchantress

Eventually Gerda manages to escape and runs off R; *the Wild Crow exits* L

Enchantress Come here! Come back! Please! Come back! Please! I'm so lonely…

The Enchantress sees Gerda's red shoes, picks them up, sighs sadly, looks offstage after Gerda, sighs again, and exits upstage

Pause

The Wild Crow enters cautiously L *and Gerda enters* R

Wild Crow It's all right. She's gone. And so've your shoes, I'm afraid. Caw!
Gerda They don't matter. Oh, thank you, Crow! I don't know what I'd have done without you.
Wild Crow (*embarrassed*) Aww! It was nothing. Really. And these children helped again, of course.
Gerda Of course they did. Thank you, children.
Wild Crow Well, now we've helped you, there's something I should've done before…

Gerda Yes?

Wild Crow Well, we haven't been introduced. That's unforgivable—helping someone when you haven't been properly introduced. Would you be so kind as to tell me your name?

Gerda Gerda.

Wild Crow (*with a little bow, trying out the name*) Gerrrda? Gerrda! I'm very pleased to meet you, Gerrda. (*He bows and offers his wing shyly*)

Gerda shakes it

Gerda And I'm very pleased to meet you—er—what's *your* name?

Wild Crow (*taken aback*) Erm—well—caw! This is a bit embarrassing. I don't know. Nobody gave me a name, you see. I'm just Crow, I suppose. I'm afraid that'll have to do.

Gerda Well, Mr Crow...

Wild Crow Just "Crow", if you don't mind—I don't think I'm a Mister.

Gerda Well, Crow, what'll we do now?

Wild Crow We! Cawww! We?

Gerda Well—you're going to help me look for Kai, aren't you?

Wild Crow Caw! I'm only an old Crow!

Gerda But what a *wonderful* Crow!

Wild Crow (*embarrassed*) Aww! Caww! Well, I'll do my best—I swear by my Grandmother's tail feathers.

Gerda (*remembering*) Oh! My poor Grandmother—she must be wondering where I am! But I'll soon go back home—with Kai. Crow, you seem to be a wise old bird...

Wild Crow (*flattered*) Aaaaw! Caw!

Gerda Have you heard anything about him?

Wild Crow Maybe, maybe!

Gerda (*excited*) He's alive? (*She hugs the Wild Crow*)

Wild Crow (*apparently put out, but really pleased*) Stop that! Please! You'll ruffle my feathers. Now be sensible. I said I *might* have seen Kai—but if it *is* him, I'm afraid he must've forgotten you because of the Princess.

Gerda A princess! Does he live with a princess now?

Wild Crow Yes, he does. Er—I suppose you don't speak crow language? I really prefer speaking it, you know, 'cos it's much easier than yours.

Gerda I've never learned it. But I think my Grandmother does—and she sometimes speaks double Dutch. I wish she'd taught me.

Wild Crow Never mind, it can't be helped. I'll do my best. Now, to begin at the beginning (*shyly*) I'm engaged to be married...

Gerda Oh, Crow! Congratulations!

Wild Crow (*embarrassed*) Thank you. Caaw! Now, my fiancée's another crow. Well, of course she is, 'cos birds of a feather flock together, you know. Anyway, she's tame and she lives in the palace, and *she* told me this story. I'll tell you as we go along. In this kingdom…

Gerda and the Wild Crow exit L

The Little Trolls clear the stage and exit as the Old Troll enters R *and speaks to the audience*

Old Troll Listen—this is the story the Crow told Gerda. In this kingdom, where we are just now, there lives a princess who's terribly clever. She reads all the newspapers in the world and forgets what's written in them, and that proves how clever she is. Anyway, a few weeks ago she was sitting on the throne—and some people seem to think that's rather a funny place to sit—when she happened to think "I want to get married". The problem was finding someone who was as clever as she was. She didn't want somebody who'd just stand about looking handsome without a word to say for himself. Well, one day a fellow came to the palace to see her. He said he'd come to find out if she was as clever as everybody said she was. So they chatted for a while, and she *was*! So he was pleased. And *he* was as clever as *she* was, so *she* was pleased. In fact, they were *so* pleased, that in the end…

The Old Troll exits L *as Gerda and the Wild Crow enter* R

Wild Crow …In the end they got married, you see. My fiancée says he talks as well as I do when I talk crow language.

Gerda It *must* be Kai! He's so clever he can do arithmetic in his head. He can even work out fractions! So he married the Princess…

Wild Crow Well, if I wasn't a crow, *I'd* have married her—even though I'm engaged!

Gerda Will you take me to the palace?

Wild Crow Caw! That's easy—'cos here we are.

Gerda Let's go in!

Wild Crow *That's* not so easy! They don't allow just anybody in. Tell you what, I'll go and talk to my fiancée, she might know how we can do it. But I can tell you—it won't be easy…

Gerda I *will* get in! Anyway, as soon as Kai knows I'm here, he'll come and get me himself.

Wild Crow Wait here—and stay out of sight.

The Wild Crow exits upstage

Gerda hides

Two toy Soldiers carrying popguns enter from opposite sides of the stage

First Soldier Halt!
Second Soldier Halt!
First Soldier Who goes there?
Second Soldier Who goes there?
First Soldier I asked first!
Second Soldier You didn't! I did!
First Soldier Didn't!
Second Soldier Did!
First Soldier Let's try it again. You go over there, right?

The Soldiers cross to opposite sides of the stage. Pause. They suddenly turn, each hoping to catch the other one out

(*Fractionally ahead*) Who goes there?
Second Soldier Who goes there?
First Soldier I asked first! Again!
Second Soldier Didn't!
First Soldier Did!
Second Soldier Didn't.
First Soldier Right, try again.

The Soldiers stand back to back and then cross towards opposite sides of the stage. The First Soldier turns before he reaches his side

Who goes there? See! See! I asked first!
Second Soldier That wasn't fair! Do it again.

They stand back to back. As the Second Soldier crosses to his side of the stage, the First Soldier follows close behind him. As the Second Soldier turns, the First Soldier is already pointing his popgun under the Second Soldier's nose

First Soldier (*triumphantly*) Who goes there? I did it again! I asked first!
Second Soldier (*furious*) You cheated! (*He stamps away*)

The First Soldier stands uncertainly

First Soldier Let's do it again.
Second Soldier Nah.
First Soldier Why not?
Second Soldier Don't want to. I'm fed up. Let's do the next bit.
First Soldier Right.

Second Soldier You start.
First Soldier Right. Halt! Who goes there?
Second Soldier I do, you fool.

The First Soldier stands uncertainly

First Soldier Oh! Er—what's next?
Second Soldier (*sotto voce*) Friend or Foe?
First Soldier What?
Second Soldier (*sotto voce*) Friend or Foe?
First Soldier I can't hear you. What're you whispering for?
Second Soldier (*shouting*) Friend or Foe?
First Soldier There's no need to shout—I'm not deaf, you know.
Second Soldier (*hissing*) Just say "Friend or Foe?"
First Soldier Why?
Second Soldier So you know if I'm friendly or not.
First Soldier Oh. (*He pauses*) Are you?
Second Soldier Am I what?
First Soldier Friendly.
Second Soldier Course I am. I'm your pal, aren't I?
First Soldier That's all right, then. (*He stands uncertainly*)
Second Soldier (*sotto voce*) Go on then.
First Soldier What?
Second Soldier (*sotto voce*) Ask me who I am.
First Soldier Oh. Well—er—who are you?
Second Soldier (*exasperated, shouting*) Friend or Foe!
First Soldier I'm fed up with this. It's stupid.

Pause. The First Soldier whistles idly, then stops

What'll we do now, then? Play cards?
Second Soldier Can't do that—we're on duty.

Pause. The First Soldier whistles loudly, then has a brilliant idea

First Soldier How about a sing-song?
Second Soldier (*dismissively*) Nah. Can't sing.

The First Soldier whistles idly, then stops—he's had another brilliant idea

First Soldier Would you like to dance?
Second Soldier Who with?
First Soldier Me.

Second Soldier (*outraged*) You what! Dance! We can't do that—we're *blokes*!
First Soldier Oh, yes. Sorry.

The two Soldiers stand uncertainly

The Sergeant enters

Second Soldier Halt! Who goes there?
Sergeant Duty Sergeant.
First Soldier Friend or Foe?
Sergeant Friend.
Second Soldier Advance, Friend, and be recognized.

The Sergeant steps forward. The Soldiers look him up and down

First Soldier (*to Second Soldier*) D'you recognize him?
Second Soldier (*to First Soldier*) No. (*To Sergeant*) Who are you?
Sergeant It's me, you fools!
First Soldier How do we know it's you?
Sergeant Because you know who I ham, laddie!
Second Soldier Ah! We know who you're *supposed* to be...
First Soldier But you could be someone else who *looks* like him.
Sergeant Looks like him? Looks like who?
First Soldier Like you.
Sergeant But I *ham* you. I mean, him. Me!
First Soldier How do *we* know that?
Second Soldier You could be in disguise.
Sergeant Why should I be in disguise?
First Soldier You could be trying to break into the palace.
Sergeant (*wheedling*) Oh, come on, chaps, stop messing about.
Second Soldier You never know, you know.
First Soldier Nope! You never ever know.
Sergeant (*angry*) Right! That's enough! Stop this nonsense or you'll be on a charge!
First Soldier (*annoyed*) Aw, Sarge!
Second Soldier It was just a bit of fun.
Sergeant It may be a bit of fun to you, laddie, but I'm not putting up with it.
First Soldier But Sarge, there's nothing to do.
Second Soldier There never is!
Sergeant Nonsense, laddie, nonsense—there's plenty to do. Hatten—shun!

The Soldiers stand to attention and wait for orders. Long pause as the Sergeant searches for inspiration. Finally he gives up

You're right. Stand easy, men. I'll have to think about this.

They stand uncertainly. First Soldier whistles idly then stops—the Sergeant's had a brilliant idea

Wait a minute! There *is* something we can do.
First Soldier What?
Sergeant We could make our rounds.
Second Soldier Our rounds?
Sergeant Go round and round the gardens…
First Soldier (*brightly*) Like a teddy bear…
Sergeant No! Not like a teddy bear! Like soldiers! Right youse two! Get fell in! On the double! Hatten—shun! Shoulder—harms! Head up, heyes front, shoulders back, stomach in.

The Soldiers follow his orders into exaggeratedly awkward positions

Haaabout turn! Quiiiick—wait for it, wait for it—quiiiiick march—left, right, left, right…

The Sergeant and the Soldiers exit R

Gerda comes out of hiding

The Wild Crow enters upstage

Wild Crow Caw! I bring you greetings from my fiancée, and a piece of bread from the kitchen. Now, she says it's impossible to get in the front way. You've got bare feet, you see, and the flunkeys won't allow it. But my fiancée knows where the key for the back door's kept…

The Wild Crow's fiancée, the Tame Crow enters upstage

Ah, here you are, my dear. This is Gerda. (*Shyly*) Gerda, this is my fiancée.
Tame Crow (*shyly, but very refined, curtsying*) How do you do, young lady?
Gerda (*politely, curtsying*) I'm very well, thank you. How are you?
Tame Crow (*curtsying*) I'm exceedingly well. Thank you very much for asking.
Gerda (*curtsying*) Pleased to meet you.
Tame Crow (*curtsying*) And *I'm* pleased to meet *you.*
Gerda (*curtsying*) Thank you.
Tame Crow (*curtsying*) Likewise, I'm sure. I'm so glad you're well. It would be so very distressing to discover your journey has had an adverse

effect upon you, wouldn't it? I'm delighted to make your acquaintance. It's so rare to meet a charming young lady such as yourself. My dearly beloved fiancé's told me so many marvellous things about you. He's narrated your curriculum vitae, as it's called. I've found your adventures incredibly interesting, and your story's extremely affecting, if I may venture to mention. It's touched my heart, as they say, and I'd be delighted to help you in any way if it lies within my power to be of assistance. Now, if I understand correctly, you're desirous of entering this imposing establishment—is that not the case?

Gerda Yes please, if it's not too much trouble.

Tame Crow No trouble at all. It's entirely my pleasure, I do assure you. In any case, I think it would be most appropriate at this point in the proceedings to attempt to find shelter from the elements as it appears there's the possibility of a degree of precipitation in the area, and under the circumstances one can't possibly stay outside all night, can one? We'll be up first thing in the morning to look for your friend, naturally, because the early bird *does* catch the worm, doesn't it? (*Hastily*) Not that I'm referring to your friend as a worm, of course. I was merely employing a figure of speech by way of illustration, you understand. Please forgive me, I meant no offence.

Gerda Of course you didn't. I'm not offended at all.

Tame Crow (*relieved, curtsying*) You're so kind. Now, I'll walk ahead and show the way. We'll go as the crow flies—it's much shorter, I always find. If you'd like to come this way, please. (*She curtsies and points a wing offstage*)

Gerda (*curtsying*) After you.

Tame Crow (*curtsying*) Not at all. After you.

Gerda But I don't know the way.

Tame Crow Oh, of course not. How silly of me. I do apologise. Most profusely. (*She curtsies*) If you'd like to follow me, please. This way.

The Tame Crow, Gerda and the Wild Crow exit R

The Sergeant and the Soldiers enter L

Sergeant Left, right, left, right. Halt! Stand at—hease!

First Soldier Sarge! Sarge!

Sergeant Yes?

First Soldier I thought I saw something.

Sergeant Where?

First Soldier Over there.

Second Soldier You're right. Someone moving in the shadows.

Sergeant Right then, right then—what're you waiting for?

First Soldier What d'you mean?
Sergeant The drill, laddie, the drill!
Second Soldier Oh, right! Halt! Who goes there?
First Soldier Halt! Or I shoot!
Sergeant (*taken aback*) Steady, laddie, steady! We don't want any bloodshed now! Hey! You there, hadvance and be recognized!

Gerda, Wild Crow and the Tame Crow enter R

What's hall this then? A wee lassie and two crows. Well, well, well.
First Soldier Well, well, well.
Second Soldier Well, well, well.
Sergeant Trying to break hinto the Palace, eh?
First Soldier Eh?
Second Soldier Eh?
Gerda I'm sorry. It's my fault. I only wanted to get in to see Kai.
Sergeant Kai? Who's he?
Gerda My friend. He's disappeared and I'm looking for him…

The sound of fanfare, off

First Soldier Half a mo'. Look, Sarge, over there.
Second Soldier The Princess is coming…
First Soldier With the Prince.
Gerda It's Kai! At last!
Sergeant Hattenshun! Present harms!

The Sergeant and the two Soldiers spring to attention as music plays

The Lords, Ladies, Gentlemen, Courtiers, Ladies-in-Waiting, Gentlemen-in-Waiting, Ladies' Maids, Handmaids, Housemaids, Parlour-maids, Chambermaids, Scullery-maids, Lackeys, Flunkeys, Footmen, Servingmen, Servants, Servants' Servants, and the Servants' Servants' Boy all flood on to the stage from all available entrances, talking at the tops of their voices, and effectively blocking the way of the Princess and the Prince who are trying to enter UC

Princess Excuse me, excuse me.
Prince Gangway, please. Let us through!

Nobody takes any notice, but the Princess and the Prince eventually manage to struggle towards the front of the crowd, turning upstage to shout above the uproar

Princess Quiet please! Quiet!
Prince Quiet!

The crowd finally quieten down. The Princess and the Prince turn round and step forward

Gerda (*wailing*) It isn't him! It isn't Kai!

The crows stand either side of Gerda and comfort her

Princess What's happening here?
Prince What's the matter?
Gerda My friend's disappeared, and I've been looking for him. The crows told me about the Prince, and I thought he was Kai. But he isn't.
Prince No, I'm afraid I'm not. Sorry…
Gerda Now I don't know where to look! I'll have to start all over again.
Princess What a shame! You poor dear thing.
Prince What about these crows? Why are they here?
Princess Yes, good thought, my dear. Why *are* they here?
Gerda I wanted to get into the palace to see if Kai was here. They were only helping me.
Wild Crow (*curtsying*) I'm sorry, Your Highness.
Tame Crow (*curtsying*) It was for the best. I know we shouldn't have…
Princess One isn't angry with you, dear Crow.
Prince You were only trying to help.
Princess It was clever of you to come in by the tradesmen's entrance.
Prince Indeed it was. You should be proud of what you've done.
Princess (*mock-severely*) As long as you don't help strangers creep into one's palace too often, of course!
Tame Crow (*curtsying*) Of course, Your Majesty.
Prince But you must be tired out.
Princess Of course! How clever of you to think of it, my dear. Where's our Ladies-in-Waiting?

Identical twin Ladies-in-Waiting step forward

Ladies Here, Your Highness.
Princess Make up a bed for—you haven't told me your name.
Gerda Gerda.
Princess Make up a bed for Gerda…
Prince And ask Cook to prepare something to eat. You must be hungry.
Princess Of course you must. A good thought, my dearest.
Prince Thank you, my dearest.

Gerda Yes, thank you, your Highness.
Princess (*to Ladies-in-Waiting*) So, food and a bed. Off you go.
Ladies Very well, Your Highness.

Ladies-in-Waiting exit upstage, pushing through the crowd

Princess We'll decide what's to be done in the morning.
Prince What a very intelligent idea, dearest…
Princess Yes it is, isn't it? One always believes one thinks better after a good night's rest…
Prince Yes, we agree absolutely…

The Princess and the Prince exit upstage, chatting cleverly, almost knocked over as the Lords, Ladies, Gentlemen, Courtiers, Ladies-in-Waiting, Gentlemen-in-Waiting, Ladies' Maids, Handmaids, Housemaids, Parlour-maids, Chambermaids, Scullery-maids, Lackeys, Flunkeys, Footmen, Servingmen, Servants, Servants' Servants, and the Servants' Servants' Boy crowd towards the upstage exits, followed by Gerda and the Crows

Sergeant (*turning to the audience*) I think I hought to hinform you lot that it's the hinterval. (*He salutes the audience, and turns to the Soldiers*) Right then, youse two! Hattenshun! Shoulder harms! Head up, heyes front, shoulders back, stomach in. Haaaabout turn! By the left—quiiiick march! Left, right, left, right…

The Sergeant and the Soldiers exit upstage as——

——the Lights fade to Black-out

ACT II

Fanfare

The Sergeant and the Soldiers enter upstage, followed by the Lords, Ladies, Gentlemen, Courtiers, Ladies-in-Waiting, Gentlemen-in-Waiting, Ladies' Maids, Handmaids, Housemaids, Parlour-Maids, Chambermaids, Scul- lery-maids, Lackeys, Flunkeys, Footmen, Servingmen, Servants, Servants' Servants, and the Servants' Servants' Boy. The Princess, Prince, Gerda, and the Crows struggle through the crowd. Gerda is wearing new travelling clothes with fur boots and a fur muff

Princess You're welcome to stay with us, Gerda, you know that.
Gerda Thank you, your Highness, but I must find Kai. I *have* to go on. You've given me warm clothes and a new pair of boots—and the muff'll keep my hands so warm.
Prince Yes, a clever idea of yours, my dear.
Princess Well, one always thinks if one's *hands* are warm, the rest of one's bound to be warm as well.
Prince An excellent thought.
Gerda I've everything I need. Thank you for your kindness.
Prince My dear, perhaps we could ask the Sergeant to travel with them for a few miles, and see them safely on their way.
Princess A perfectly *marvellous* idea. Sergeant!

The Sergeant leaps to attention with a crashing of boots

Sergeant (*bawling at the top of his voice*) Sah! I mean, Ma'am!
Princess Take two men and accompany Gerda to our borders. See her safely on her way and return to us.
Sergeant (*bawling*) Sah! I mean, Ma'am! Squad! Squad! Hatten—shun! Right then, volunteers. You and you! One pace forward—step!

The two Soldiers step forward

(*Shouting*) Stand at—hease!
Princess Thank you, Sergeant.
Sergeant Sah! I mean—Ma'am!

Prince Thank you, Sergeant. Perhaps next time, a little less noise?

Princess A *very* good idea, my sweet.

Sergeant (*almost quietly*) Ma'am! I mean, Sah! Ma'am! (*He leaps back into place with a great crashing of boots*)

Princess Now, Gerda, is there anything else one can do?

Gerda No, thank you, you've been more than kind. (*She turns to the Crows*) And thanks for your help, dear friends—I'll miss you. (*She hugs the Tame Crow*)

The Tame Crow is obviously pleased, but overcome with embarrassment

Tame Crow Gently, please, young lady. I've just preened my feathers!

Wild Crow Caw! I'll come with you for a few miles, just to make sure you're all right.

The Prince whispers to the Princess

Princess What a lovely thought. An excellent idea!

Prince Ahem. Before you go, there's something one needs to say. My dear, perhaps you'd like to…?

Princess Yes, good idea. We think, for their loyalty, these Crows deserve to be rewarded. Crows—step forward.

Tame Crow (*curtsying*) Your Highness?

Wild Crow (*curtsying*) Your Majesty?

Princess Tell us, would you like to be free to fly away, or would you prefer to be given permanent positions at our court—as Royal Crows?

Prince With all crumbs and other leftovers from the kitchen table, of course.

Princess (*aside*) I'd forgotten that, my dear. Clever of you to think of it.

The Crows whisper together, then both curtsy to the Princess

Wild Crow If you please, Your Highness, we'd prefer positions at court.

Tame Crow After all, we have to consider our declining years. We'd like to have something comfortable and be well provided for because, though health is better than wealth, to be safe and secure is better than to fly, and it's good to have something laid aside for a rainy day, isn't it? A little nest egg, as it were.

The Crows look shy at the thought of nests and eggs

Princess Very well—your wish is granted.

The Crows whisper together, then both curtsy to the Princess

Wild Crow And—er—there's something else. Caw!
Princess Yes?
Wild Crow We'd—er—we'd like to—er—get married, Your Highness.
All (*amazed*) Cor!
Princess (*clapping her hands delightedly*) Of course! It'll be lovely! It's not often there's a crow wedding in the palace. My husband and I will make all the arrangements.
Prince There now, everything seems to be settled. Good luck, Gerda.
Princess You're welcome at one's palace whenever you wish.
Prince Perhaps when you've found Kai you'll return and tell us.
Princess Of course.
Gerda I will. And thank you again.
Princess All our good wishes go with you. Farewell.
Prince Farewell. (*To Princess*) What a good idea, my love. I wish *I'd* thought of it.
Princess It was really you who put it into one's mind, my dear.
Prince How nice of you to say so...

The Princess and the Prince exit upstage, chatting cleverly and complimentarily, but their dignified exit is spoiled as they are almost knocked over by the Lords, Ladies, Gentlemen, Courtiers, Ladies-in-Waiting, Gentlemen-in-Waiting, Ladies' Maids, Handmaids, Housemaids, Parlour-maids, Chambermaids, Scullery-maids, Lackeys, Flunkeys, Footmen, Servingmen, Servants, Servants' Servants, and the Servants' Servants' Boy who are all stampeding to the exits

Gerda How nice they were, and so helpful.
Wild Crow Will you come with us, dear?
Tame Crow I don't think so, my dearest. For some incomprehensible reason I've had a headache since I took up the post of Royal Crow, and I don't think a long journey would help. I'm tame, you know, and I'm not used to being out and about. And besides, I think I've eaten too much—my stomach's quite upset, it really is. But you must go. Go with Gerda—and not just for a few miles. You must stay with her as long as she needs your help.
Wild Crow (*pleased, but trying not to show it*) Are you sure, my dear?
Tame Crow I can read you like a book, dearest. I know you want one more incredible adventure before you settle down to your retirement. You're still a wild bird at heart and I know you prefer to be outdoors. Just make sure you look after the young lady.
Wild Crow I will.
Tame Crow And take good care of yourself.
Wild Crow I will. When I come back, my love, we'll be married.

The Crows hug each other shyly

Gerda (*to the Tame Crow*) I can't thank you enough, dear Crow! (*She hugs the Tame Crow*)

The Tame Crow is delighted but embarrassed

Tame Crow Oh, dear, oh dear, oh dearie, dearie me. I've really done nothing, nothing at all. You're too kind, my dear girl, too kind. Be assured my thoughts will be with you wherever you go. I'll think of you constantly— and of my dear fiancé, of course.
Gerda Thank you. Well, let's be on our way.
Sergeant Right, men—hatten-shun! Escort, escort—by the left, quick march! Left, right, left, right...

The Sergeant and the Soldier exit L with Gerda

The Wild Crow and the Tame Crow gaze into each other's eyes and slowly move apart, touching wing tips for as long as possible. Finally the Wild Crow turns decisively and exits L, as the Tame Crow waves goodbye sadly and exits R

The Old Troll enters upstage with the Little Trolls who set the Snow Queen's throne C

Old Troll Now, what's become of Kai? Listen—imagine this is the Snow Queen's ice palace. The walls are snowdrifts, and the icy winds have blown out holes for windows and doors. Here, there's never been a dance for polar bears, or a party for young white lady foxes. Neighbours are never invited round for coffee, with something to eat and a little bit of gossip—or even a game of cards. Enormous, empty, and bitterly cold is the Snow Queen's palace of ice. And here comes the Snow Queen herself...

The Old Troll and Little Trolls exit R as Ice Attendants enter from UL with a huge tray. They stand aside as the Snow Queen enters from UL with Kai

Snow Queen This is my palace. Isn't it beautiful?
Kai Oh, yes! Where does the light come from?
Snow Queen From the northern lights. They burn so brightly they can be seen from far away.
Kai Is this your throne?
Snow Queen It is.
Kai Sit on it. Please. I'd like to see what a real Queen looks like.

The Snow Queen sits on her throne. Kai sees the tray L

What's that?
Snow Queen It's a Magic Mirror. The most magical mirror in all the world.
Kai But it's all broken! It's in thousands of pieces. (*He looks closer*) They're all exactly the same! Like snow flakes.

The Snow Queen rises and crosses to Kai

Snow Queen Look closer. You can play a game. You must put the pieces together to make a pattern, and if the pattern spells a word—a special word—you'll be your own master.
Kai What's the word.
Snow Queen You'll know when you find it.
Kai That's impossible!
Snow Queen Is it? Try. Now listen carefully, if you find the special word, I'll give you the world—and a pair of ice skates.
Kai But I can't...
Snow Queen Try it, Kai, just try. You never know what you can do till you try.

Kai becomes absorbed in the puzzle as he tries to put the pieces together. The Snow Queen watches him for a while

(*To the audience*) I almost pity him. He's half frozen but doesn't feel it. His heart's a lump of ice. He thinks what he's doing's so important, but it's just like playing with wooden bricks, and he could do that when he could barely talk. How foolish these humans can be! As long as he thinks about my puzzle he's mine. But that's enough for now. Kai, come and explore my palace. There are a hundred halls—some of them are miles long! Come!
Kai Can I bring the puzzle?
Snow Queen Yes, bring it and come with me.

The Snow Queen and Kai exit. The Ice Attendants follow with the tray

The Little Trolls enter and take the throne off

Gerda and the Wild Crow enter R

Gerda Well, we're on our own again. Pity the soldiers couldn't have stayed with us.
Wild Crow Caw! They had their "horders". (*He imitates the Sergeant and marches up and down*) "Right lads, hat the border—turn! Quick march!

Hat the double—left, right, left, right!" Caaaw! And I thought *crows* were noisy!

Gerda (*laughing*) Dear Crow! Still, I felt safe when they were with us.

Wild Crow (*a bit put out*) Caw!

Gerda Now, now, you *know* I feel safe when *you're* with me, don't you?

Wild Crow (*doubtful*) Caw!

Gerda I do! I do! I really really do!

Wild Crow (*pleased*) Caw!

Gerda This forest's very dark. Are we going in the right direction, do you think?

Wild Crow (*concerned*) You're tired. Tell you what, you sit here and rest. I'll fly ahead a little way and see what's what and what's where.

The Wild Crow starts an unsteady take-off, wildly flapping his wings, and exits L

Gerda I'm so lucky. All the animals and humans I've met have helped me...

The Robber Band, outlandishly dressed and with obviously false bushy beards and eyebrows, leap out from various entrances and surround Gerda, trying to look ferocious but failing miserably

First Robber Ha!
Second Robber Ha!
Third Robber Ha!

The Robbers stand expectantly, looking at Gerda. She doesn't react. They look at each other and try again

First Robber Ha!
Second Robber Ha!
Third Robber Ha!
Gerda (*fed up with this*) Ha yourselves!

The Robbers leap back a pace, and look at each other uncertainly

First Robber Ain't you 'fraid of us?
Gerda Should I be?
Second Robber We're wicked 'n' fewocious wobbers.
Third Robber We're gonna take all yer gold.
First Robber N'en we'll prob'ly kill yer!
Gerda Oh!
Second Robber Z'at all yer c'n say?

Gerda What happens if I don't have any gold?
Third Robber We'll prob'ly kill yer.
Gerda Oh.
First Robber We'll prob'ly kill yer anyway.
Gerda Oh!
Second Robber We us'lly do.

Pause as the Robbers look at each other for inspiration

First Robber You got'ny gold?
Gerda No.
Second Robber Jools?
Gerda No.
Third Robber Money?
Gerda No.
First Robber Valu'bles?
Gerda No.
Second Robber Nuffink at all?
Gerda No. Not worth stealing, anyway.
Third Robber Oh.

Pause as the Robbers look at each other for inspiration. They have Gerda cornered downstage and form a half-circle round her

First Robber Well, wot'll we do now, then?
Gerda Kill me?
First Robber S'pect so.
Second Robber We us'lly do.
Third Robber We kill ev'rybody.
First Robber Most of the time.
Second Robber Us'lly.
Third Robber We kill 'em all.
First Robber Dead.

The Old Hag enters L. She is incredibly old and also has a false beard and even bushier eyebrows

The Robber Girl enters UR, but stays in the background, gradually moving forward during the following dialogue

The Old Hag pushes through the Robbers

Old Hag Wot we got 'ere, then?

First Robber This 'ere girl…
Second Robber But she don't 'ave no gold…
Third Robber Or jools…
First Robber Or money…
Second Robber Or valu'bles…
Third Robber She ain't got nuffink…
First Robber She ain't got nuffink nohow…
Second Robber Not nowhere, she ain't…
Third Robber N' she ain't 'fraid 'f us, neither.
Old Hag Aha! Not afraid, eh? Ha, ha, ha! Let's 'ave a look at yer. (*She pinches Gerda's arm*) She's lovely…
First Robber Lovely 'n' fat!

The Robbers think this is incredibly funny, and laugh uproariously

Old Hag Nah, she's pretty…
Second Robber Pwetty well-fed!

The Robbers roar with laughter

Old Hag Well-dressed…
First Robber Dressed ter kill!

The Robbers fall about

Old Hag Like a little fat lamb!
Second Robber A lamb ter the slaughter!

The Robbers are almost helpless with laughter

Old Hag Bet she'll taste as good as lamb once she's been cooked! (*She advances on Gerda*)

The Robber Girl pushes through the Robbers, leaps at the Old Hag and bites her. The Robbers back away as the Old Hag and the Robber Girl confront each other

Ouch! Wicked child! Yer bit me ear!
Robber Girl The girl's for me!
Old Hag Fer *you*! What yer want wiv 'er?
Robber Girl I don't have no friends me own age—I want to play with her! An' I always get me own way!
Old Hag Nasty little brat!

The Robber Girl bares her teeth and snarls. The Old Hag and the Robber Girl circle each other, snarling and hissing

Robber Girl Try an' stop me an' I'll bite your ear right off! Go away!

The Old Hag and the Robbers withdraw upstage to a safe distance and stand scowling

    (*Satisfied*) I *always* get me own way! (*She looks Gerda up and down and points at Gerda's muff*) What's that fur thing?
Gerda It's for keeping your hands warm. You put them inside, see?
Robber Girl I want it. Hand it over!

Gerda gives the muff to the Robber Girl

    It's lovely and soft. Your dress is pretty. I'll have that too, when I'm ready. You got lovely things. You a princess?
Gerda No. My friend Kai's disappeared and I'm trying to find him so I can take him home. He's only little and I love him very much.
Robber Girl You better forget about him. You're staying with me 'cos you're my prisoner. Anyway, *they* won't let you go.

The Robbers snarl in the background

Gerda Will they kill me?
Robber Girl I won't let 'em—s'long as you don't make me angry. Anyway, if I *do* get angry I'll prob'ly kill you meself.
Gerda But I must find my friend!
Robber Girl I'm your friend now. Mebbe if I get tired of you I'll let you go. You can meet me other friend, if you like. (*She calls off*) Here, me old sweetheart, c'mere!

An old Reindeer enters, with a rope round its neck

During the following, the Robbers get things ready for a feast

    He's me favourite. He'd like to run away, but he can't. You have to hold on to him, though, or he'd be off. I keep prickling him with me dagger— that keeps him quiet. (*She takes out her knife and pokes the Reindeer's neck with it*) Hah! Frightened of me, ain't you! Kiss me! (*She pulls the Reindeer's head round*)

The Reindeer slurps against the Robber Girl's cheek

What a lovely big slobbery kiss! Mmmmm! I love you! C'mere. (*She throws her arms round the Reindeer's neck and hugs him, then takes him to a downstage corner and ties him up*)

Gerda Do you always carry a knife?

Robber Girl Always! You never know what might happen. An' I always get me own way. You hungry?

Gerda Yes.

Robber Girl S'pose you want summat to eat.

Gerda Yes, please.

Robber Girl Come on then. Sit there.

The Robbers have got everything ready. They eat and drink, sing and dance. After the dance everyone prepares for sleep

(*To Gerda*) I'm gonna tie you up. Try 'n' get away, an' I'll have to prickle you with my knife. You c'n sleep there. Here's a blanket. Lie down—and keep quiet! (*She ties Gerda up, covers her with a blanket, and lies near her*)

The Reindeer sleeps standing up in a downstage corner. The Old Hag lies down in the other downstage corner. Business as the Robbers make a rough tent from branches and an old blanket, but when they try to get in the whole thing collapses. The Robbers finally give up and settle down under cover of the blanket. The Lights dim. Various resounding snores in sequence from the Old Hag and the Robbers establish an almost musical rhythm. Eventually there is silence

The Wild Crow enters L, *cautiously*

Wild Crow (*to the audience*) Caw! Ssssh! Excuse me. Can you tell me— quietly—if Gerda's here? Where is she? Ah! Ssssh! Caw!

Following the audience's instructions, and with much "Shushing", the Wild Crow creeps over to Gerda, and gently wakes her

Gerda What is it?

Wild Crow Sssh!

Gerda (*whispering*) Crow! I thought I'd lost you!

Wild Crow (*whispering*) I thought *I'd* lost *you*!

Gerda Where have you been?

Wild Crow I met some wood pigeons—they've seen little Kai!

Gerda (*loudly and excitedly*) Where?

There is a chorus of snores from the Robbers

Wild Crow Ssssh!

Gerda (*quietly*) Where?

Wild Crow He was in the Snow Queen's sleigh when it flew over the forest. She breathed on them and all the baby chicks died.

Gerda (*loudly*) Oh, no! How dreadful!

Chorus of snores from the Robbers

Wild Crow Ssssh!

Gerda (*quietly*) Where was she going?

Wild Crow The pigeons think she was going to Lapland. There's always snow and ice there. I've never been, but you could ask the Reindeer over there.

Gerda Ask the reindeer! (*Scornfully*) Reindeer can't talk.

Wild Crow Crows aren't supposed to talk either—but *I* do! Caw!

Gerda I hadn't thought of that...

Wild Crow Anyway, you won't know if you don't ask.

Gerda crawls over to the Reindeer, who's pretending to be asleep

Gerda Reindeer! Reindeer! Can you talk?

Reindeer (*opening one eye*) Talk? Of course I can talk! D'you think I'm just a dumb animal? (*He opens both eyes*) I heard everything you said. (*He sighs wistfully*) Yes, there's always snow and ice in Lapland—it's a wonderful place.

Gerda What about the Snow Queen? Will she be there?

Reindeer Well, she spends the summer there, but her winter palace is way way off near the North Pole.

Gerda (*loudly*) I must go there!

Chorus of snores. The Robber Girl, wakened by the voices, rises

Robber Girl What's going on?

The Reindeer pretends to be asleep

The Wild Crow cautiously exits

(*Angrily*) Do I have to cut someone open?

Gerda The Snow Queen's got Kai. She's taken him to Lapland. Where's Lapland?

Robber Girl Reindeer!

A big snore from the Reindeer

I *know* you're awake!

The Reindeer makes a big show of waking up

Reindeer Snort! Wassat? Wassappening?
Robber Girl I *know* you heard ev'rything, 'cos *she* talks so loudly, and *you're* always eavesdropping. Do you know where Lapland is?
Reindeer Who'd know better than me? That's where I was born—in the great snowfields—the icy plains—the frosty wastes...
Robber Girl Quiet! You want me to prickle your throat? (*To Gerda*) I don't know why, but I'm gonna help you. Listen. They'll all go soon. Mama won't, but I'll make her take a drink and have a little nap. Now—lie down till the others wake up. And keep quiet!

Gerda and the Robber Girl lie down. It gets brighter. The Robbers wake, grumbling, and gather all their equipment

First Robber Look alive, you lot—we gotter lotter robbin ter do.
Second Robber It's fweezin! Can't we light a fire?
First Robber No, we can't light a fire!
Third Robber I'm starvin! Got'ny food?
First Robber No! N' if we don't get robbin pretty sharpish we won't get none neither.
Second Robber Not nohow we won't.
Third Robber Not never.
Second Robber Not nohow.
Third Robber Never ever.
Second Robber We never ever does.
Third Robber S'always the same.
Second Robber Fweezin—no fire!
Third Robber Starvin—no food!
Second Robber N' no money!
First Robber Shurrup and come on! Yer like a load 'v ole wimmin!

Still grumbling, the Robbers exit R

Robber Girl They've gone. Stay here. (*She rises, crosses to the Old Hag and pulls her beard to waken her*) Morning, old nanny goat! Aren't you gonna have a little drink?
Old Hag (*drowsily*) Mmmn—nnm—namamm.

The Robber Girl holds the bottle to the Old Hag's lips and pours the drink down her throat

Nnnmamma—nnn—mmm. Ah! (*She falls asleep, and starts snoring*)

Robber Girl There, never takes long. Reindeer! C'mere! I love prickling you with me little dagger, 'cos you're so funny when I do, but I'm gonna let you loose so's you can go back to Lapland. You're to take Gerda to the Snow Queen's palace an' help her find her friend. Got it?

Reindeer (*nodding excitedly*) Yes. Of course. Certainly.

Robber Girl That's enough of that! I'm gonna untie you.

She unties the Reindeer, who leaps about delightedly

I know you're pleased, but stop bouncing all over the place. (*To Gerda*) You can have the boots 'cos it's cold where you're going. I'm keeping the muff, though—it's pretty. I'll give you me mother's mittens instead— they'll keep you warm all right. (*She takes the Old Hag's fur mittens and gives them to Gerda*) Here, put 'em on. Now your hands look ugly like me mother's! Well, you'd better not wait any longer. (*To the Reindeer*) Take care of the little girl. I'll miss you. (*She hugs the Reindeer fiercely*) Well, it's time to wake up the old nanny goat. Wait till we've gone, right?

The Robber Girl crosses to the Old Hag, kicks her to waken her and helps her stagger off R

The Wild Crow enters

Wild Crow Have they gone? Is it safe?

Gerda Quite safe, dear Crow. And the Reindeer's going to come with us. Well, which way do we go?

Reindeer We'll head towards the northern lights—over there. Look! It's a long cold journey, so the sooner we start the better. Come on—follow me!

The Reindeer bounds off L *like a huge puppy, comes back to make sure they're following, and bounds off again, followed by Gerda and the Wild Crow*

Kai enters from upstage, puzzling over the mirror on the tray being carried by the Ice Attendants

Kai I *must* solve this puzzle! The trouble is, every time I think I'm getting somewhere, the pieces move by themselves and spoil it…

The Snow Queen enters

Snow Queen Ah! Here you are. Still playing the game?

Kai Tell me what the word is, please!

Snow Queen Ah! You'll find it when you solve the puzzle. Keep at it, my boy, keep at it! (*Calculatingly, with an eye on Kai*) I'm off to see some volcanoes—to look into their big black boiling cauldrons! I'll put a touch of ice on their peaks—it'll freshen them up a bit. Do you want to come?

Kai (*not looking up*) No—I've got to finish this...

Snow Queen (*triumphantly*) Once he would have jumped at the chance of seeing a volcano—but as long as he's lost in my puzzle, here he'll stay! Wherever it goes, he will follow. Attendants, bring the puzzle! Come!

The Snow Queen exits UL

The Ice Attendants exit upstage with the tray, and Kai follows

A small Penguin walks across the stage from R *to* L

Gerda, the Reindeer and the Wild Crow enter R

Gerda Is this really Lapland?

Reindeer Of course. Dear old Lapland—I'd recognize it anywhere.

Wild Crow Caw! It's freezing!

Gerda It's so cold I can hardly talk!

Wild Crow How on earth can anyone live here?

Reindeer It's wonderful! Snow and ice everywhere—dazzling and glittering. It warms my old heart no end.

Wild Crow It doesn't warm my end! Cawww! My poor old tail feathers are frozen! I hope they don't drop off!

The Lapp Woman enters L, *carrying a stove and a basket of dried fish. She is very short-sighted and has to peer at them closely*

Lapp Woman Who's there? Who's that?

Reindeer Three weary travellers. We're searching for the Snow Queen's palace.

Lapp Woman Oh, you poor poor things. You've a long way to go yet. It's hundreds of miles from here to Finland and the Snow Queen's camp.

Gerda We've come so far already! How do we know she's even there?

Lapp Woman When she is, she lets off fireworks every night. I've seen them, flashing and flickering all over the sky. She's there all right—I always know.

Gerda What'll we do?

Lapp Woman Ah, my dear, that's a hard question and no mistake. That needs a great deal of thought, to be sure, and we have other fish to fry.

You're cold and hungry. Have some fish while I have a little think. (*She gives them fish*)

They sit on the ground to eat

Now, tell me, my dear—why do you want to find the Snow Queen, anyway? It's dangerous to meddle with her, you know.

Gerda She's stolen my friend. She took him away in her sleigh, and we've travelled hundreds of miles to get him back.

Lapp Woman Oh, you poor sweet child. That's a pretty kettle of fish you've landed yourself in, and no mistake. A pretty kettle of fish indeed. Now, what to do? What to do? (*She pauses*) Ah! I'll tell you what—I'll give you an introduction to the Finnish Woman who lives in the North. She knows more about the Snow Queen than I do. If there's something fishy going on, she'll spot any red herrings, I'm sure of it. She'll be able to help you, I've no doubt. Now, I don't have any paper, so I'll write on this dried codfish. (*She writes on the codfish and gives it to Gerda*) Now don't lose this, my dear, whatever happens. I'm sorry it's all I can do. I'd help more if I could.

Gerda Thank you. You've been so kind.

Lapp Woman Well—we never know when we'll need help, do we? If we can't be friendly to people we can't expect them to be friendly to us, now can we? And you may be able to help *me* some day.

Reindeer Well, I suppose I'm in charge, so we'd better get going.

Lapp Woman Good luck—and be careful. Perhaps on your way back you'll stop and tell me how you got on.

The Reindeer, Gerda and the Wild Crow exit L

The Lapp Woman waves goodbye and exits R

The small Penguin crosses the stage from L to R with a fishing pole over its shoulder

The Old Troll enters. As he speaks, the Little Trolls arrange a collection of stools, and a small stove with a pot of cooked fish on it

Old Troll They travelled farther and farther north. And as they went it got colder and colder. The snow and the ice stretched for miles, as far as the eye could see. The northern lights flickered and flared—they were the Snow Queen's fireworks, you see. They followed the old woman's instructions, and at last they reached their destination...

The Old Troll and the Little Trolls exit

The Finn Woman enters L *with several blankets round her shoulders*

The Reindeer enters R

Finn Woman Ah! Here at last.
Reindeer I beg your pardon?
Finn Woman I said "Here at last".
Reindeer That's what I thought. What do you mean?
Finn Woman I mean I've been expecting you.
Reindeer How did you know we were coming?
Finn Woman I always know when someone's coming. Where are the others?
Reindeer They're just behind. They can't travel as fast as I can. They're not used to the snow, so I came on ahead.

Gerda and the Wild Crow enter R

Wild Crow Help me—Gerda's exhausted.
Finn Woman Come in, come in. Oh, my poor little one, you're so cold! Put this blanket round you and get warm. (*She wraps a blanket round Gerda*)
Reindeer I'm warm already—it's rather hot in here.
Finn Woman Take your coat off. Oh, of course, you can't. Here, put this on your head. (*She ties a lump of ice on to the Reindeer's head*)
Gerda Are you the Finnish woman?
Finn Woman I am. You'll be hungry—have some fish.
Wild Crow Everyone offers us fish. Are you sure there isn't anything else?
Finn Woman No.
Wild Crow You wouldn't happen to have the odd worm, I suppose?
Finn Woman No.
Wild Crow Well, it's not a crow's favourite food, but thank you anyway. Caw!

They sit on the stools, and the Finn Woman gives them fish

Finn Woman So! A little girl—a reindeer—and a crow. An odd collection of friends indeed. How can I help?
Gerda The Lapp woman gave me this for you. (*She gives the Finn Woman the dried codfish*)

The Finn Woman sniffs it, bites it, holds it to her ear, shakes it, then looks at it closely

Finn Woman Ah! I see! This explains everything. You're looking for the Snow Queen, is that right?

Gerda Yes. She's stolen little Kai. We're going to take him back home.

Finn Woman Easier said than done, little one.

Gerda Can you help us?

Finn Woman (*ignoring her*) I'll save this codfish—I'll be able to boil it for my breakfast. Mustn't waste anything, must we? (*She puts the fish in her pot*)

Gerda tries again

Gerda Please...

Finn Woman (*kindly*) Come, little one, sleep for a while. You're tired. We'll talk later, when you've rested. (*She spreads a blanket in a downstage corner for Gerda*)

Gerda takes off her boots and mittens and lies down. The Wild Crow arranges the blanket as the Reindeer takes the Finn Woman aside

Reindeer Listen, you're very wise. I know you tie all the winds of the world into four knots. If a sailor unties one knot, he gets a breeze; if he unties the second there's a wind; the third knot makes the wind get stronger, but if he unties the fourth there's such a storm his ship is wrecked. If you can do that, why can't you give this little girl the strength of ten men so she can fight the Snow Queen?

Finn Woman The strength of ten men! That wouldn't be enough! It wouldn't go any way at all! (*She turns away, muttering*)

The Reindeer shakes his head sadly and goes to stand in a corner. The Wild Crow goes to the Finn Woman impatiently, and takes her aside

Wild Crow Can't you help Gerda—or *won't* you? I'm sorry to be angry, but she's travelled so far for so long—she'll never give up. Please help her!

Finn Woman She's captured your heart, there's no doubt. And our old Reindeer friend would do anything for her. (*She pauses*) All right, I'll tell you what I know. (*She takes the Wild Crow and the Reindeer aside*) Little Kai's in the Snow Queen's ice palace. He quite likes it there, but that's because he's got a piece of glass in his heart and another in his eye. Until he's got rid of them he'll be just like a child, and the Snow Queen will keep him for ever.

Wild Crow Can't you give Gerda something to take the pieces of glass out?

Reindeer Or some kind of power to beat the Queen?

Finn Woman She already has great power—I can't give her any more. You two must feel it or you wouldn't be here.

Reindeer What d'you mean? I don't feel anything...

Finn Woman Think! Everyone she's met has helped her. How else could she have come so far?

Wild Crow Caw! I've got it! Her power makes people want to help her!

Reindeer And animals! Don't forget the animals! And the birds, of course.

Finn Woman You see—you had the answer all along. You yourselves are the living proof. But she can only use her power because she's still a child—if she knows of it, her innocence will be gone and her power will be useless. She *can* set Kai free, but only *she* can do it—and she must do it alone. She must go on from here without you. She must enter the Snow Queen's palace by herself.

Reindeer If she can't get into the palace, how can we help?

Finn Woman If she *can't, no-one* can help her.

Wild Crow Whatever happens, we'll do everything we can!

The Finn Woman starts to take the lump of ice off the Reindeer's head

Finn Woman So! Here's what we *can* do. Reindeer, the Queen's palace is a mile from here. Take Gerda there, and come right back.

Reindeer But...

Finn Woman (*sharply*) Just do it, Reindeer. (*Gently*) Just do it. (*She wakens Gerda*) It's time to go, little one. The Reindeer will take you on the last part of your journey.

Gerda But what...

Finn Woman Go now.

The Reindeer exits L with Gerda on his back

The Finn Woman and Wild Crow watch them go and then exit R

The Little Trolls enter and remove the stools

The small Penguin crosses the stage from R to L, carrying the fishing pole and a few fish

Kai enters from upstage with the Ice Attendants carrying the puzzle tray. They set the tray down L and go aside as Kai kneels and arranges the pieces

The Old Troll enters UC

Gerda enters R

The Old Troll is between Gerda and Kai

Old Troll Listen—we must return to little Kai. He isn't thinking of Gerda.

He's forgotten her. And even if he could remember, he wouldn't think she could be right outside the Snow Queen's ice palace. She's forgotten her boots, she's forgotten her mittens, but there she stands in the arctic cold—alone. (*He steps aside*)

Gerda sees Kai and runs to him

Gerda Kai! My little Kai! I've found you!
Kai (*without looking up*) I don't know you!

The Old Troll exits

As Gerda throws her arms round Kai, the Snow Queen enters upstage, unseen by Gerda

Gerda You're so cold—you're frozen!
Kai Go away! Leave me alone! (*He pushes her away and goes back to his puzzle*)
Gerda (*sadly*) Kai, I've found you at last—and you don't know me!
Snow Queen What are you doing here?

Gerda turns and faces the Snow Queen

Gerda I'm Gerda—Kai's friend.
Snow Queen (*sharply*) I know who you are, child—I asked what you were doing here.
Gerda I've come to take him back.
Snow Queen Take him back? You? (*She laughs*) Tell me, how did you get here? How did you cross my wilderness of ice and snow?
Gerda I walked.
Snow Queen In bare feet!
Gerda Yes.
Snow Queen To find your friend?
Gerda Yes.
Snow Queen But why? Why?
Gerda I want to take him home—where he belongs!
Snow Queen (*to Kai*) You don't want to go home with this girl, do you?
Kai No. *This* is my home—and I don't know her! Anyway, I want to finish my puzzle!
Snow Queen You see, child? He belongs *here*! Your journey's a wasted one. Go back while you can—unless you wish to stay with me for ever!
Gerda (*defiantly*) I won't go without Kai. I've travelled hundreds of miles to get here and I'm not leaving without him!
Snow Queen Hundreds of miles in your little bare feet—all by yourself?

Gerda No! I've found good people and animals to help me.
Snow Queen Yet you face me alone. You must be very brave.
Gerda I'm not brave. (*Simply*) I love Kai.
Snow Queen Well then, what's he worth to you? Would you fight for him?
Gerda (*bravely*) If I have to.
Snow Queen (*amused*) Very well. Let's see what you think of my creatures.
Come, my icy ones! Come and see who wishes to fight you!

She steps aside as her terrible and hideous Ice Creatures enter

*As they advance, Gerda steps back to protect Kai. The Snow Queen and
Gerda face each other across the width of the stage*

Well, my child. What can you do now? Against these?
Gerda (*quietly*) I can only pray. (*She kneels beside Kai and bends her head*)

*The Ice Creatures continue to advance, but Gerda's Guardian Angels
appear and gather round her*

The Ice Creatures and the Guardian Angels battle with each other

*The Ice Creatures are finally defeated, leaving the stage to the victorious
Guardians, who acknowledge Gerda and exit*

*The positions of Gerda and Kai, the Snow Queen and the Ice Attendants are
as before. Gerda rises and faces the Snow Queen*

It's all over. You're beaten.

The Snow Queen moves aside and stands silently for a moment

Snow Queen Yes, little one, there's no doubt you have power of some sort.
(*She pauses*) Very well, take him—if you can. His icy heart won't let him
leave. Why, he doesn't even recognize you!
Gerda (*turning to Kai*) Kai! Kai! You *must* know me. You must! (*She kneels
and puts her arms round Kai*)

*He doesn't respond, and sits motionless, staring at the puzzle. The Snow
Queen laughs and turns away. Pause. Gerda continues to hug Kai until
finally he stirs*

Kai (*wonderingly*) I feel—warm! I feel as if my heart's melting…

The Snow Queen turns in surprise and alarm

What's happening to me? (*He seems to come out of his trance and looks at Gerda*) Gerda! Gerda! Is it really you?

Gerda Yes.

Kai Where have you been so long? (*He rises and moves* c) Where am I? It's so empty here—and so *cold*!

The Snow Queen crosses to Kai, and takes his face in her hands. She looks closely into his eyes

Snow Queen The ice in your eye has melted! But what of your heart?

Kai It's not cold any more. I feel warm again.

The Snow Queen is taken aback. She turns abruptly, steps away and thinks desperately

Snow Queen Don't forget your puzzle.

Gerda Kai! No! Leave it!

But Kai turns to the puzzle tray and kneels down beside it

Snow Queen I see it now, child. Your love was strong enough to melt the ice in his heart, but he still can't come with you—he hasn't finished the puzzle...

Kai (*in triumph*) But I have! Now I can see clearly again—I've found the word!

Snow Queen No!

Gerda Tell her, Kai—tell her! What is it?

Kai slowly rises and faces the Snow Queen

Kai (*triumphantly*) Eternity!

Snow Queen (*sighing*) Aaaah! Eternity.

Kai Is it right?

Snow Queen (*sadly*) Yes. You're right. You've found it. I meant you to search for eternity—until the end of time.

Kai You promised me the whole world and a pair of ice skates!

Snow Queen Do you want the whole world?

Kai No—I wouldn't know what to do with it. I'd like the skates, though.

Gerda (*defiantly*) He's *found* the right word—give him his freedom! You promised!

Snow Queen (*suddenly angry*) You've one more problem to solve—how to leave my halls! Attendants, seize them!

The Attendants seize Gerda and Kai and drag them aside

The Wild Crow enters, flapping his wings

Wild Crow Gerda, I'm here! I couldn't let you face her alone. Caw! (*He stands in front of Gerda, spreads his wings, and faces the Snow Queen*) Caw! Let her go!
Snow Queen You won't stop me!

The Snow Queen suddenly points at the Wild Crow who staggers, falls and lies still

Gerda (*heartbroken*) Crow! Crow!
Snow Queen Take them to my dungeons!

As the Attendants step forward, the Reindeer enters

Reindeer Reindeer to the rescue! Release them, you ruffians! (*He charges the Attendants and scatters them, standing between Gerda and Kai to protect them from the Snow Queen*)
Snow Queen Another friend! Suppose I kill you, too?
Reindeer There'll be another, and another!
Gerda Lots more. More than you can imagine.
Snow Queen (*angrily*) That's enough!
Gerda (*despairing*) We've done everything! What more can you want!

The Snow Queen raises her hand for silence. She crosses to the completed puzzle and stands looking down at it. Pause. Finally she turns away and moves DL *to stand alone*

Snow Queen (*with resignation*) You're right—you've done all I asked. I shouldn't have been angry. Whatever I could have done doesn't matter any more. Kai's right to freedom is written in the pieces of ice. *Your* right to freedom is in the love of your friends.

Gerda kneels by the Wild Crow

Gerda One of my friends is dead! He can't have *his* freedom.
Snow Queen (*thoughtfully*) He must have loved you very much.
Gerda He did. I didn't realize. I didn't know how much!
Snow Queen Yes, you *do* have power! Stronger than anything I have. You've succeeded when you had no right to do so. You've won the hearts of humans and animals, and if I had a heart you might have conquered me as well. As it is, you've persuaded me to help you. (*She turns to the audience*) Children, you must be the judge and the jury. This poor crow—has he been a good friend? Has he done as much as he possibly could? (*She*

listens to the audience) Very well—I have your answer. Quiet now! (*She touches the Wild Crow's head*)

The Wild Crow stirs. Gerda helps him to rise

Wild Crow What happened?
Gerda Crow! You're alive!
Wild Crow Of course I'm alive—I've got a wedding to go to! (*He leans on the Reindeer for support*)

Gerda faces the Snow Queen

Gerda Well? What happens now?

The Snow Queen turns to the audience

Snow Queen Once more *you* must judge. Has Gerda done enough to win her freedom? (*She listens to the audience, then turns to Gerda*) You've done everything you can. And more. Much more. You deserve to go home. You've won. You may go.

Pause

Go! Before I change my mind!

Gerda, Kai, the Wild Crow and the Reindeer exit R

The Snow Queen watches them go, and turns to the audience

The Old Troll, unseen by the Snow Queen, enters UR *and watches her*

I have no heart, yet even I feel something. I'm alone, and being lonely can be the worst thing of all. I have no friends, and no-one speaks to me—not even the Old Troll who started it all... (*She turns and moves upstage, pausing as she sees the Old Troll*)

The Old Troll bows slightly

The Snow Queen returns the bow, and exits UL

The Old Troll moves downstage

Old Troll (*to the audience*) And so they went home. And as they went, they met everyone who'd helped Gerda on her journey...

Gerda, Kai, the Wild Crow and the Reindeer enter and move to DC

The Tame Crow, the Princess and the Prince, the Finn Woman, the Lapp Woman, and the Robber Girl, or if doubling, as many of these characters as possible, enter and congratulate them

The Wild Crow and the Tame Crow were married...

The Tame Crow and the Wild Crow come forward

The Enchantress, the Sergeant, the two Soldiers, the Old Hag, the Robbers, and the Courtiers enter upstage and join in as everyone applauds

The friends said their last goodbyes...

Farewell hugs between Gerda, the Wild Crow and the Reindeer

And finally Gerda and Kai returned to their Grandmother.

Grandmother enters downstage

Kai and Gerda run into her arms

In their hearts they were still children, but they'd grown up. They'd forgotten the Snow Queen—as if everything that had happened had been only a bad dream.

The Little Trolls enter

Everyone turns to face the audience in a final tableau. The Old Troll reads the final words from his book

The winter was over and it was summer—a warm glorious summer. And the end was as good as the beginning. (*He closes the book*)

Everyone bows

At the last moment, the Snow Queen enters, steps forward, and smiles at the audience. She raises her arms, and it begins to snow

The Lights fade to Black-out

FURNITURE AND PROPERTY LIST

Further dressing may be added at the director's discretion

ACT I

Off stage: Door frame (**Little Trolls**)
Rocking chair (**Little Trolls**)
Small table. *On it:* picture book (**Little Trolls**)
Sledge (**Kai**)
Sledges (**Children**)
Bowl of cherries (**Enchantress**)
Little gate (**Little Trolls**)
Carpet of grass and flowers (**Little Trolls**)
Piece of bread (**Wild Crow**)

Personal: **Old Troll:** huge book
Grandmother: knitting
Snow Queen: fur cloak
Enchantress: large sun-hat decorated with flowers, flowery handkerchief, golden comb
Gerda: red shoes
Soldiers: popguns

ACT II

Off stage: **Snow Queen**'s throne (**Little Trolls**)
Large tray with mirror puzzle pieces (**Ice Attendants**)
Branches or poles and old blanket (**Robbers**)
Items of food and drink (**Robbers**)
Blanket (**Robber Girl**)
Small stove (**Lapp Woman**)
Basket of dried fish (**Lapp Woman**)
Dried codfish and piece of charcoal (**Lapp Woman**)
Fishing pole (**Penguin**)
Stools (**Little Trolls**)

Small stove (**Little Trolls**)
Pot of cooked fish (**Little Trolls**)
Lump of ice (**Finn Woman**)
Fish (**Penguin**)

Personal: **Gerda:** fur muff
               Robbers: false beards and eyebrows
               Old Hag: false beard and eyebrows
               Reindeer: rope
               Robber Girl: dagger
               Old Hag: bottle of drink, fur mittens
               Finn Woman: blankets

LIGHTING PLOT

Property fittings required: nil
Various interior and exterior settings

ACT I

To open: Overall general lighting

Cue 1	**Old Troll:** "…turn into a lump of ice!" *Snow effect*	(Page 4)
Cue 2	**Old Troll** and **Little Trolls** move into shadows *Dim lights on* **Old Troll** *and* **Little Trolls** *and fade up* *on room area*	(Page 4)
Cue 3	**Grandmother:** "…dazzling, gleaming ice." *Dim lights*	(Page 5)
Cue 4	**Snow Queen** exits *Dim lights as* **Little Trolls** *remove furniture*	(Page 7)
Cue 5	**Kai** enters *Bring up general lighting*	(Page 7)
Cue 6	**Gerda** exits *Dim lights as* **Little Trolls** *set stage*	(Page 10)
Cue 7	**Little Trolls** fade into the shadows *Bring up general lighting*	(Page 10)
Cue 8	**Old Troll** and **Enchantress** exit *Dim lights*	(Page 12)
Cue 9	**Wild Crow** enters *Bring up general lighting*	(Page 12)

| *Cue* 10 | **Gerda** and the **Wild Crow** exit | (Page 16) |
| | *Dim lights as* **Little Trolls** *clear stage* | |

| *Cue* 11 | **Little Trolls** exit | (Page 16) |
| | *Bring up general lighting* | |

| *Cue* 12 | **Sergeant** and **Soldiers** exit | (Page 24) |
| | *Fade to black-out* | |

ACT II

To open: Overall general lighting

| *Cue* 13 | **Tame Crow** exits | (Page 28) |
| | *Dim lights as* **Little Trolls** *set stage* | |

| *Cue* 14 | **Old Troll** and **Little Trolls** exit | (Page 28) |
| | *Bring up general lighting* | |

| *Cue* 15 | **Snow Queen** and **Kai** exit | (Page 29) |
| | *Dim lights as* **Little Trolls** *set stage* | |

| *Cue* 16 | **Gerda** and **Wild Crow** enter | (Page 29) |
| | *Bring up general lighting* | |

| *Cue* 17 | **Robbers** settle down under cover of blanket | (Page 34) |
| | *Dim lights* | |

| *Cue* 18 | **Gerda** and **Robber Girl** lie down | (Page 36) |
| | *Bring up to brighter lighting* | |

| *Cue* 19 | **Gerda** and **Wild Crow** exit | (Page 37) |
| | *Dim lighting* | |

| *Cue* 20 | **Kai** enters | (Page 37) |
| | *Bring up general lighting* | |

| *Cue* 21 | **Snow Queen** and **Kai** exit | (Page 38) |
| | *Dim lighting* | |

| *Cue* 22 | **Gerda**, **Reindeer** and **Wild Crow** enter | (Page 38) |
| | *Bring up general lighting* | |

Cue 23	**Lapp Woman** exits *Dim lighting*	(Page 39)
Cue 24	**Finn Woman** enters *Bring up general lighting*	(Page 39)
Cue 25	**Finn Woman** and **Wild Crow** exit *Dim lighting*	(Page 42)
Cue 26	**Gerda** enters *Bring up general lighting*	(Page 42)
Cue 27	**Snow Queen** raises her arms *Snow effect and fade to black-out*	(Page 48)

EFFECTS PLOT

ACT I

Cue 1   **Gerda**: "…I'm looking for him…"   (Page 22)
           Fanfare, off

Cue 2   **Sergeant**: "Present harms!"   (Page 22)
           Music

ACT II

Cue 3   To open   (Page 25)
           Fanfare